READY . . .

STEADY . . .

OFFICIAL GUIDE

READY . . .
STEADY . . .
GO GOS!

The world of the Gogos is crazy and extremely cool. This book is for the hardcore fans out there in need of lots of stats and facts and things to do. There's an Official Collectors' Poster, where you can see the Gogo's Crazy Bones and check out which ones you still need. On the flip side of the poster, you'll find your Battleground Mat to use with the games and challenges in this book. You can also use the mat to make up your own games.

TOP SCORERS

Every Gogo is different, Gaiji has super speed and Skull has perfect bounce and balance. Read the facts, then fill out the profile card on the opposite page for your favourite top scoring Gogo and draw a picture or stick a funny photo of it in the box.

THE GOGO GREATS FACTS

The fastest Gogos in this neck of the woods are:
Cosmic Kolo, crazy Helly, happy Sun, smiley Simi, the very cool Gaiji and - saving the best for last - Speed himself!

The bounciest bones on the block are:
Scary Skull, Nuclos, Molly, double brained Pibi, ultimate grip Fist, cunning Zar-Zar, the electric Egbot and last, but by no means least - Shizuoka.

The spookiest Gogo is:
The dark and mysterious hooded Ghost!

MY TOP SCORING GOGO:

Name: ....

Number: ....

Colour: ....

Top Ability: ....

Favourite Game: ....

Favourite Word: ....

Number of Games Won: ....

Number of Games Lost: ....

At the end of this book you may have a new top scorer, but you can fill in those details on the Winner's Certificate at the end. Only if you win, of course!

Go! Go! Gogo's Crazy Bones!

Have you and your Gogos got what it takes to make it through the toughest challenges yet? Start by taking each of your favourite Gogos through the initiation tests and contests in this book. Remember to keep a record of all yours and your friends' results using the scoring table on pages 4-5 and see who makes it to the award ceremony at the end. There are time-outs for quizzes and training, but remember, every little point you score will count in the end. You can play your own Gogos against each other or play against your friends and their Gogos. Will any of your Gogos be worthy of the Winner's Certificate? Let the adventures begin to find out!

GOGOS! Let's go!

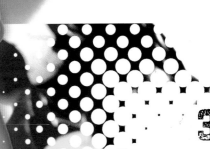

Super Scoring!

The Gogo's Crazy Bones have taken over and they're all about games, challenges and contests! Work through the tests and games in this book and fill in the score sheet with the names of your Gogos and the points they score.

GOGO & OWNER NAME	INITIATION PG 6-7 TOTAL POINTS	KNOCK 'EM OUT PG 8-9	POWER QUIZ PG 10-11	DIVING PG 12-13	FOOTBA PG 14-
LIAM alkaline					

Top Tip

Try to use a pencil, so you can rub everything out and play again and again. At the end of the challenges add up the points and fill in the total column, then put the name of the winning Gogo on the certificate on page 29. Pull out the certificate and put it on your wall.

Alternative scoring

For each test or challenge you can use an alternative scoring system. For example, play a 'joker' card and get double points for the winner of that game, deduct points for a Gogo that loses more than once, get an extra point if your Gogo bounces over a certain height in any of the challenges. But remember, whatever scoring system you have at the beginning of each challenge you must keep to the same one throughout.

IE OUT 16-17	STREET GAMES PG 18-19	TARGET PG 20-21	GRID PG 22-23	EXTREME SPORTS PG 24-25	TOTAL POINTS

THE INITIATION

Before you play any games, you must take each of your Gogos through this series of initiation tests to make sure they are true Gogos and are trained up and ready for the competition.
Will your Gogos go the distance?

You can go through the initiation tests with just your own Gogos or along with your friends.

Test 1 - The Drop

Find a brick wall and grab some chalk. Take it in turns to drop each Gogo to the floor and mark on the wall how far up the Gogo bounces upwards on its first bounce. The winner scores one point.

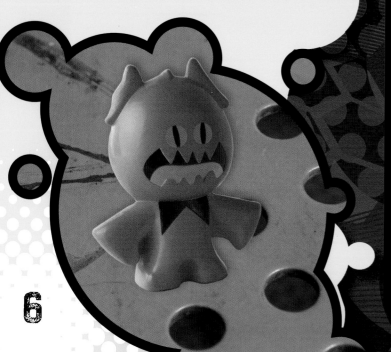

Test 2 - Going the Distance

Line up your Gogos along a starting line. Take it in turns to flick them along the ground. The winning Gogo is the one who travels the furthest along the ground. The winner scores two points.

Test 3 - Pushover!

Put your Gogos into pairs next to each other. Flick one onto the other and see how far the second one goes. (Measure the distance with a ruler) The three Gogos who manage to flick the others the furthest win 10 points each. Make sure each Gogo has a turn at being the one doing the pushing!

Scoring

Add up the points each of your Gogos scored in the tests then put them in the right column on the scoring table on the previous pages.

Did you know . . .

Hazard is one of the most determined Gogos of all. He's determined to fight and sure to win!

KNOCK 'EM OUT

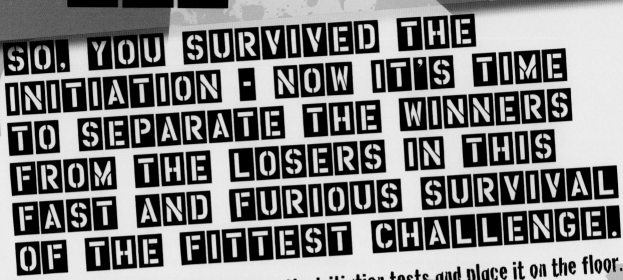

SO, YOU SURVIVED THE INITIATION - NOW IT'S TIME TO SEPARATE THE WINNERS FROM THE LOSERS IN THIS FAST AND FURIOUS SURVIVAL OF THE FITTEST CHALLENGE.

1. Choose the Gogo who scored the least in the initiation tests and place it on the floor. This is the target.

2. Stand about two metres away from the target and take it in turns to throw each of your remaining Gogos as close to the target as possible.

3. Make sure you keep an eye on which Gogos are yours. If you see another player's Gogo get close to the target, try to knock it out of the way on your next turn.

4. The winner is the Gogo that is left closest to the target after all the Gogos have been thrown.

SCORING

1. THE GOGO CLOSEST TO THE TARGET AT THE END WINS THREE POINTS.

2. THE GOGO SECOND CLOSEST TO THE TARGET WINS ONE POINT.

3. THE GOGO WHO IS THE FURTHEST AWAY IS DEDUCTED ONE POINT.

TIP: TO GET PRECISE MEASUREMENTS TO THE TARGET USE A RULER OR TAPE MEASURE.

Did you know...
Fist holds a great deal of strength in his ultimate grip.

POWER QUIZ

How much do you really know about your Gogos?
Give yourself five minutes to answer as many of the questions below as you can and gain some powerful extra points on the scoreboard. Or you could challenge a friend to see who can answer the questions the fastest.

There are clues for some of the questions hidden within this book, so try reading the whole book before you start.

The Questions
Write down the letter next to the correct answer for each question on a piece of paper. Make sure you don't show your opponent!

1. Let's start with an easy one: On which part of a Gogo will you find its number?
a. On its head.
b. In its mouth.
c. On its back.
d. Nowhere. The Gogos don't have numbers.

2. Who is the spookiest of all the Gogos?
a. Angiru
b. Ghost
c. Sun
d. Boy

3. Which one of these Gogos moves well in space?
a. Alkaline
b. Kolo
c. Vampa
d. Kola

4. Which Gogo is the most daring pirate?
a. Hiraku
b. Rufus
c. Pop
d. Dare

5. Which Gogo has an exclamation mark after his name?
a. Umu
b. Me
c. Oh
d. My

6. How many Gogos are on the poster in this book?
a. 85
b. 120
c. 52
d. 70

7. Who's ability is having an ultimate grip?
a. Speed
b. Jelly
c. Imon
d. Fist

8. In the original Gogo's Crazy Bones games, how many points do you score if your Gogo lands standing upright?
a. 1
b. 3
c. 10
d. 5

9. Who has a double brain?
a. Pibi
b. Fist
c. Raysun
d. Tremi

10. Which Gogo has two boxing gloves?
a. Mosh
b. Skull
c. Sato
d. Ghost

DIVING CONTEST

Home in on the skills and agilities of your Gogos by trying out this fantastic new dive and spinning contest. It's tumbletastic!

Line up your Gogos along the edge of a wall. Take it in turns to flick each one off, causing them to tumble to the ground. The aim is to get your technique perfected so that each Gogo does as many somersaults before it lands as possible. Keep a record of how many tumbles each Gogo does.

Scoring

1. EACH GOGO RECEIVES ONE POINT PER TUMBLE.

2. IF ANY OF YOUR GOGOS LAND STANDING UP THEY RECEIVE FIVE EXTRA POINTS.

3. TRY GAINING SOME EXTRA POINTS BY HAVING A BUCKET OR BATH OF WATER FOR THE GOGOS TO LAND IN. THE ONE WHO MAKES THE LEAST SPLASH AS IT DIVES WINS FIVE POINTS.

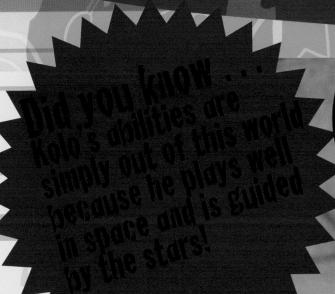

Did you know . . . Koto's abilities are simply out of this world because he plays well in space and is guided by the stars!

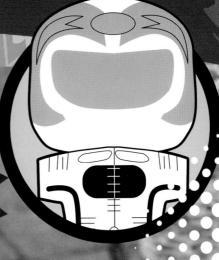

Football Madness!

All of the Gogos love a game of football to work off all that extra energy they have. Test your flicking skills to the limit in this five-a-side footie extravaganza or perfect your technique with a penalty shoot-out!

Challenge a Friend

Mark out a football pitch on the ground with one set of goal posts at either end. Scrunch up some paper into a ball and place it in the centre of your pitch. Choose five Gogos each, put one in either goal, then toss a coin to see who starts. Flick your Gogos around trying to hit the paper ball between the goal posts. Give yourself 10 minutes to play and make sure you defend your goal with one of your Gogos too!

Or play on your own

Try a penalty shoot-out with your Gogos. Use one goal and line up your Gogos about 50 centimetres from the goal. Give yourself two minutes on the clock to shoot as many goals as you can. Each Gogo scores a point for every goal it makes.

Tip - If you don't have much room to play in use the football pitch on your Battleground Mat.

Scoring

1. For the Challenge - The team with the most amount of goals at the end of the game scores one point for each Gogo.

2. For the penalty shoot-out - one point is given to each goal scored by a Gogo at the end of the two minutes.

It's a Gogo's goal!

Did you know . . .
B-Ball is the master of all that involves a ball.

TIME OUT!

Take some time out from the challenges to play a round on this board game and gain some extra points if you make it to the finish first.

Choose a Gogo each and place them on the start. Take it in turns to roll a dice and move around the board, tackling the tasks along the way. The first one to the finish is the winner and receives five extra points to go on the scoring table.

YOU WILL NEED A DICE FOR THIS GAME

1. START

2.

3. You're more than ready for action. Move on two spaces.

4.

5.

6. In a fierce battle you end up on your head. Stay here until you roll a 1 or a 6.

7.

14.

15. Your enemies take control of the game. Hop back two spaces.

13.

16.

12.

17.

11. Dare triple dares you in a challenge and you win. Bounce on three spaces.

18.

19. Speed is your friend. Move on three spaces.

20.

21. You're frozen to the spot. Stay here until you roll a 3 or a 5.

10.

23.

22.

24. Your technique is perfect and you ace every move. Move on one space.

9.

25.

26.

8. You knock out all your opponents in a bowling contest. Roll again.

27.

30. FINISH!

28.

29. Your super cool move fails and you fall on your face. Move back two spaces.

STREET GAMES

These are challenges for the toughest and most street-wise Gogos with serious attitude. You don't need anything other than your Gogos and yourself. Unless you want to challenge a friend.

Chuck 'n Catch!

Put three Gogos on the back of your hand, chuck them up into the air and turn your hand around ready to catch them as they come back down.

Scoring

Each Gogo you catch receives three points.

Fingers and Fours

Turn your hand palm up and balance a Gogo on each of your fingers. Throw them up into the air at least 30 centimetres high and try to catch as many as you can. The ones you catch are the winners. Do this once for all of your Gogos on your score table.

Scoring

Each Gogo you catch receives two points.

Balance

How many Gogos can your balance on top of each other in a stack before they fall over?

Scoring

You get one point for each Gogo in your stack.

Spinning

Put each Gogo on the ground and spin it as fast as you can. How many times does it spin around?

Scoring

Receive one point for each full revolution.

Extra points

If your Gogos land standing upright in any of the above games, give them an extra five points.

Did you know ...

Ichiro has the toughest street cred out there. He can out wit anyone he comes across with the power of his stare.

TARGET PRACTISE

EVERY GOGO NEEDS TO KEEP IN TOP SHAPE, PRACTISE THE PERFECT BOUNCE AND NAIL LANDINGS. USE YOUR BATTLEGROUND MAT TO HELP YOU WITH TARGET PRACTISE AND PRECISION SCORING. IT'S BOUND TO HELP YOU IN THE FUTURE AND YOU NEVER KNOW WHEN YOU'LL NEED THE EXTRA BIT OF HELP AGAINST THE TOUGH COMPETITION OUT THERE.

PUT THE TARGET SECTION OF YOUR BATTLEGROUND MAT ON THE FLOOR. STAND ABOUT TWO METRES AWAY FROM THE MAT. THROW EACH OF YOUR GOGOS ONTO THE TARGET AND AIM FOR THE BULL'S EYE. HAVE THREE PRACTICES FOR EACH GOGO AND WRITE DOWN THE HIGHEST SCORE FOR EACH ONE ON YOUR SCORING CHART.

SCORING

USE THE NUMBERS ON THE TARGET FOR YOUR SCORING. FOR EXAMPLE, IF YOU LAND ON THE OUTER RING YOU DON'T GET ANY POINTS. IF YOU LAND ON THE CENTRE OF THE CIRCLE - THE BULL'S EYE - YOU GET 10 POINTS AND SO ON.

10 5 3 2 1 0

Did you know . . .
Fujichik is very motivated and lands with perfection.

GRUELING GRID

Use the other side of your Battleground Mat to play this great grid game.

Choose six of your highest scoring Gogos so far (or three each if you have an opponent) and line them up at the bottom of the grid. Take it in turns to flick the Gogos onto the grid and use the chart opposite to see how many points your Gogo gets for where it lands. Watch out for the black holes or you're out of the game and won't get any more turns! Wherever you land you must stay until your next go. Each Gogo has a total of five flicks on the grid.

Scoring

Use the coordinates below to get your scores,
then put the points for each Gogo on the scoring
table after you have had five flicks on the grid.

A:I= 1	B:I= Hole	C:I= 5	D:I= 2	E:I=1	F:I= 1	G:I= 2
A:II= 3	B:II= 1	C:II= Hole	D:II= 1	E:II=1	F:II= 3	G:II= 5
A:III= 4	B:III= 3	C:III= 4	D:III= 4	E:III= 2	F:III= Hole	G:III=2
A:IV= Hole	B:IV= 2	C:IV= 1	D:IV= 5	E:IV= 5	F:IV= 1	G:IV= 3
A:V= 1	B:V= Hole	C:V=1	D:V=3	E:V= Hole	F:V= 5	G:V= 4
A:VI= 5	B:VI= 4	C:VI= 3	D:VI= 5	E:VI= 2	F:VI= 1	G:VI= Hole

Note: You must not land on the same square as
another Gogo and if you knock them out the way,
you must put them back! If you land on more than
one square, you receive points for the one you are
on the most. If you are on more than one square
equally, then you must flick again.

EXtreme Sports

Finish off the contest with two intense adrenalin-filled head rushes. Which of your Gogo participants will excel at these extremely difficult tasks?

Bungee Elastic!

Attach one end of a metre length of elastic to your Gogo. Hold on to the other end of the elastic and drop your Gogo to see how high it bounces back up. Try this with all of your Gogos. The one who springs back up to the highest level is the winner.

Scoring

The Gogo who springs up the highest is the winner and receives five points. The second highest receives three points and the third one point. The remaining Gogos do not gain any points on the scoring table.

Base to Base!

Set up a row of three upturned plastic plant pots or cardboard boxes. There should be a gap of at least 30 centimetres between each one. Try to flick each Gogo from one pot or box to the next, landing on the top. The smaller the pot or box is, the more difficult the target landing spot will be, so if you want to test yourself to the limit use smaller landing platforms.

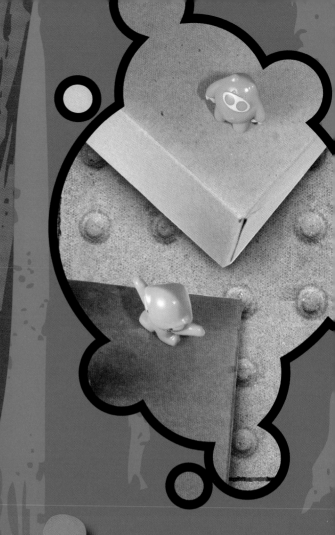

Scoring

Each Gogo who makes it to the end of the bases receives five points. Each Gogo who makes it to just one of the bases gets two points.

Did you know . . .
Helly is perfect for everything extreme. He's incredibly fast and his helmet helps make him streamline.

THE GOGO TIMES

DECEMBER ?????   BRINGING YOU THE NEWS ON THE GOGO   VOLUME NO. 4 567 898

THE GOGO'S AWARDS

The time has finally come to announce the winners of the very prestigious Gogo's Crazy Bones Awards. Who will it be? Read on to find out.

Richard Renshaw Tennis McCourt was born in a barn at the age of seven months and has never closed a door in his life. Before he became a master of the theatrical arts, Dick tried his hand at various artistic pursuits.

At the age of two, he was a stand-up comedian, touring the hard Working Men's Clubs of Britain. Dick

without stabilisers. In no time at all, he became an expert in both these fields and he was able to become a normal school boy.

Dick was a grade A (for average) student. But nothing could stop the stars that twinkled in this boy's eyes. At the age of 18, Dick dazzled a Professor at his University interview by performing

His most successful play, however - the one that would gain him worldwide notoriety, if not critical acclaim - was A musical satire on a television chat show, the piece contained 8,000 references to musk and three hundred uses of the word Norris.

The follow-up was loved the Danish Prince through for the of its palace and the world

himself - under very heavy make-up.

He played the part for umpteen years until the pressure of putting A duvet up his jumper and yelling "To be, no beauties!" before keeling over every night (and twice on A Saturday) simply became too much. Dick left the business of show Turtles

THE HIGHEST SCORING GOGO AND WINNER OF THE OFFICIAL GOGOS AWARD IS:

THIS IS TO CERTIFY THAT

....

....

HAS THE HIGHEST SCORE OF

....

....

STICK A PIC OF YOUR GOGO HERE

GOGO'S OFFICIAL WINNER

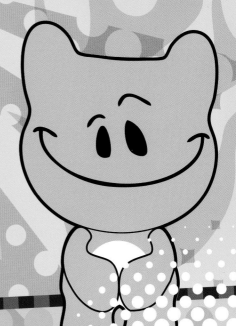

FILL IN THE NAME OF YOUR GOGO'S CRAZY BONES WINNER ALONG THE DOTTED LINES.

Pages 10-11 Quiz Answers

1. c On its back
2. b Ghost
3. b Kolo
4. a Hiraku
5. c Oh (Oh!)
6. a 80
7. d Fist
8. d 5
9. a Pibi
10. c Sato

MOST WANTED

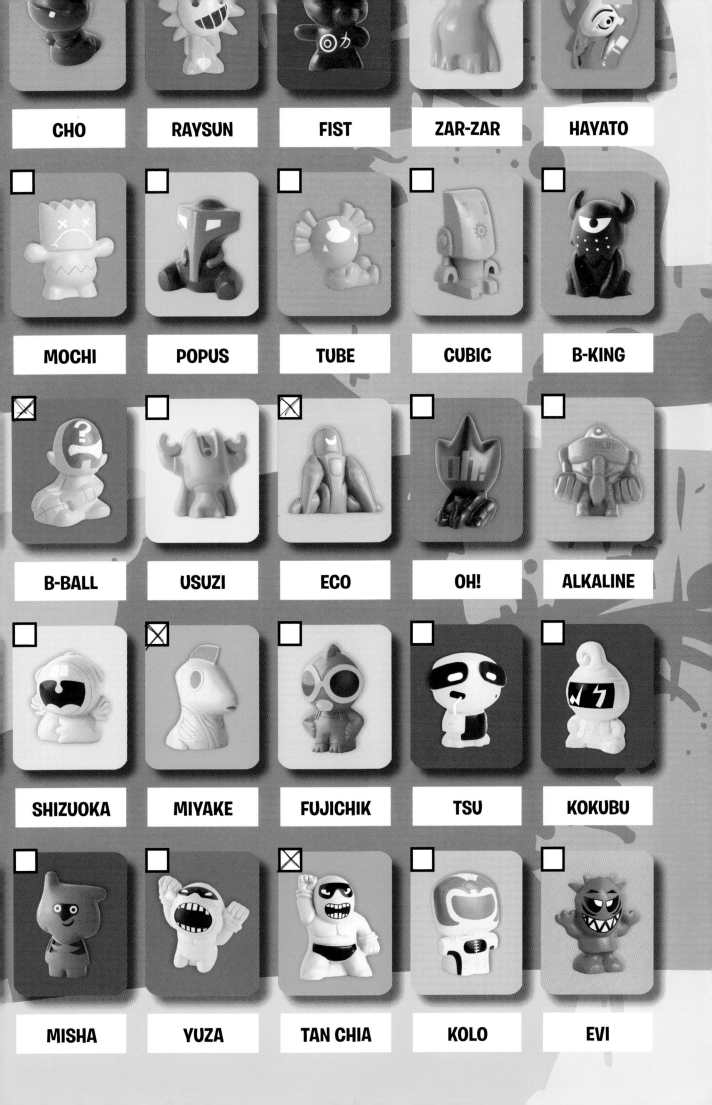

CHO   RAYSUN   FIST   ZAR-ZAR   HAYATO

MOCHI   POPUS   TUBE   CUBIC   B-KING

B-BALL   USUZI   ECO   OH!   ALKALINE

SHIZUOKA   MIYAKE   FUJICHIK   TSU   KOKUBU

MISHA   YUZA   TAN CHIA   KOLO   EVI

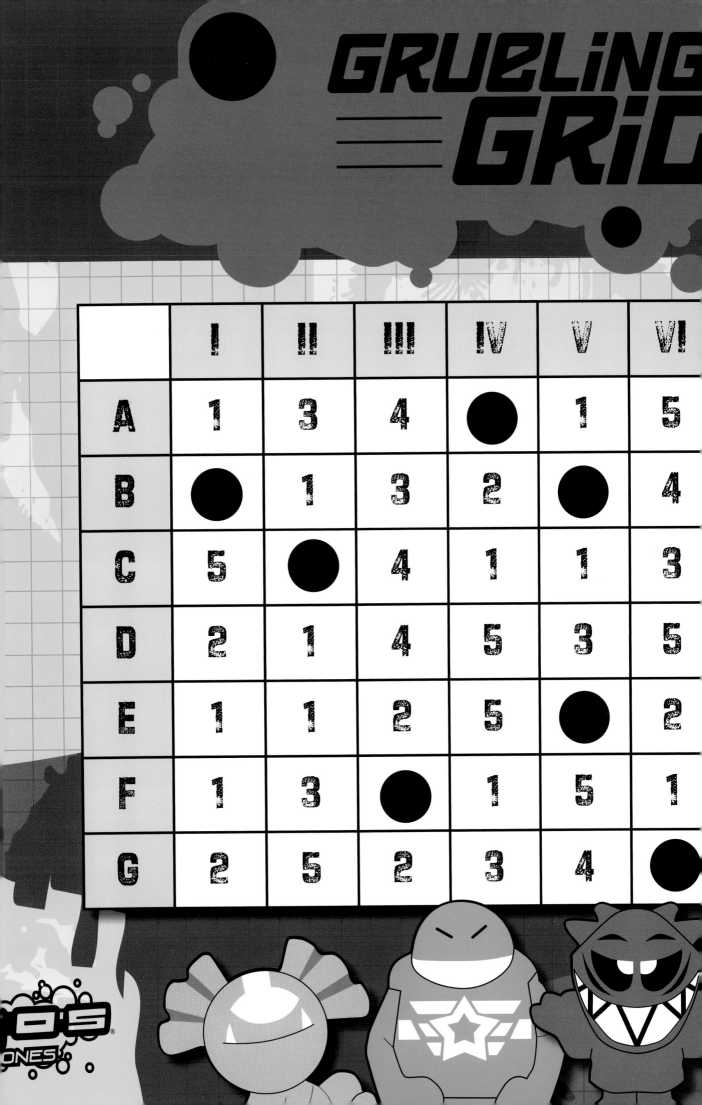

PUT A TICK IN THE WHITE BOX NEXT T

☐
MOSH

☐
NASAKO

☐
SATO

☐
OKORI

☐
TORI

☐
ICHIRO

☒
NUCLOS

☐
BOY

☒
NEKO

☐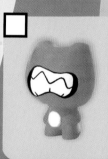
HAZARD

☐
SIMI

☐
CODI

☒
HIRAKU

☐
RUFUS

☐
TEMP

☐ ☐ ☐ ☐ ☐

Football Madness!

MOST WANTED

ANGIRU

ICHIRO

HIRAKU

FIST

B-BOY

EACH GOGO'S CRAZY BONES YOU HAVE.

HELLY

SKULL

ANGIRU

UMU

AIKO

SUN

HIRO

AKA

MOLLY

NARI

PIBI

DARE

DANKO

MC TOY

GAIJI